DUDLEY SCHOOLS
LIBRARY SERVICE

KU-337-492

Schools Library and Information Services

S00000722675

The Enormous Turnip

retold by Robert James

Illustrated by Mark Chambers

FRANKLIN WATTS
LONDON•SYDNEY

First published in 2009 by
Franklin Watts
338 Euston Road
London
NW1 3BH

Franklin Watts Australia
Level 17/207 Kent Street
Sydney
NSW 2000

DUDLEY PUBLIC LIBRARIES

L - - - - -

722675   SCH

JJ

Text © Franklin Watts 2009
Illustration © Mark Chambers 2009

The rights of Robert James to be identified as the author
and Mark Chambers as the illustrator of this Work have
been asserted in accordance with the Copyright, Designs
and Patents Act, 1988.

All rights reserved. No part of this publication may be
reproduced, stored in a retrieval system, or transmitted
in any form or by any means, electronic, mechanical,
photocopy, recording or otherwise, without the prior
written permission of the copyright owner.

A CIP catalogue record for this book is available
from the British Library.

ISBN 978 0 7496 8606 2 (hbk)
ISBN 978 0 7496 8612 3 (pbk)

Series Editor: Jackie Hamley
Series Advisor: Dr Barrie Wade
Series Designer: Peter Scoulding

Printed in China

Franklin Watts is a division of
Hachette Children's Books,
an Hachette UK company.
www.hachette.co.uk

Once upon a time, an old farmer and his wife grew turnips on their farm.

One of the turnips
looked enormous.

5

"I'll pull up that enormous turnip now," said the farmer.

"Yes, then we can have turnip soup for supper," agreed his wife.

The farmer gave the enormous turnip a gentle tug.

But the turnip did
not move.

The farmer pulled
and pulled.

Still the turnip did
not move.

The farmer called to his
wife for help.

The farmer and his wife
pulled and pulled.

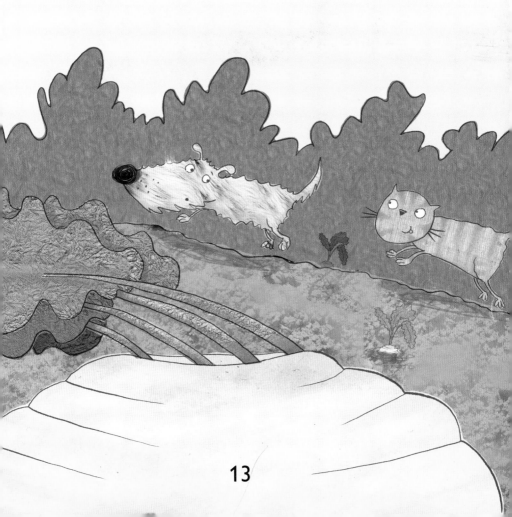

Still the turnip did
not move.

The farmer's wife whistled
to the dog for help.

16

The farmer, his wife and
the dog pulled and pulled.

Still the turnip did
not move.

So the dog barked
to the cat for help.

The farmer, his wife,
the dog and the cat
pulled and pulled.

Still the turnip did
not move.

"It's no good. This turnip is stuck!" sighed the farmer.

Then the cat meowed to
a little bird for help.

The farmer, his wife,
the dog, the cat and the
little bird pulled and
pulled and pulled.

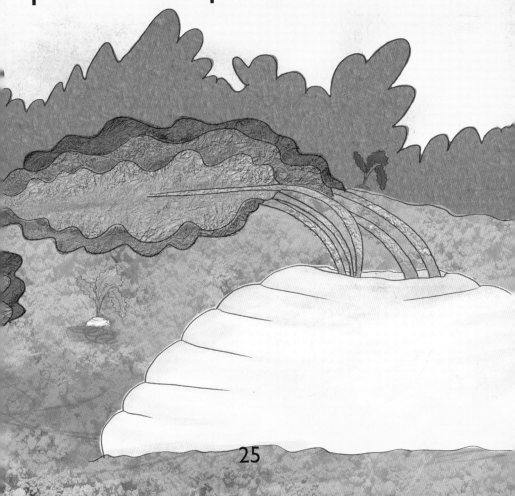

Up came the
enormous turnip
with an enormous
POP!

27

Then they all had turnip
soup for supper ...

and breakfast,

and
lunch,

and tea!

Puzzle 1

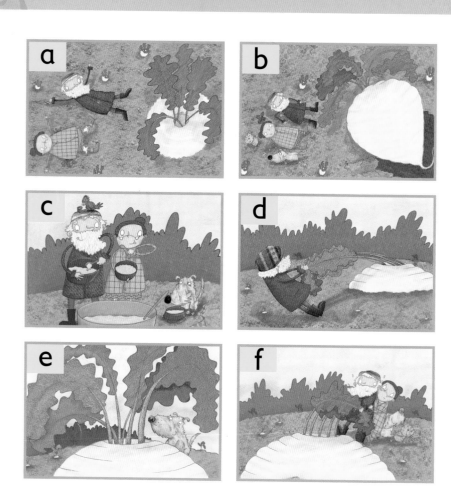

Put these pictures in the correct order.
Now tell the story in your own words.
What different endings can you think of?

Puzzle 2

young   old
hardworking

lazy   strong
helpful

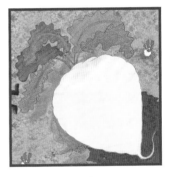

tiny   huge
minute

Choose the correct adjectives for each character or object. Which adjectives are incorrect? Turn over to find the answers.

Answers

Puzzle 1

The correct order is: 1e, 2d, 3a, 4f, 5b, 6c

Puzzle 2

Farmer: the correct adjectives are hardworking, old

The incorrect adjective is young

Farmer's wife: the correct adjective is helpful

The incorrect adjectives are lazy, strong

Turnip: the correct adjective is huge

The incorrect adjectives are minute, tiny

Look out for Leapfrog fairy tales:

* hardback

For more Leapfrog books go to: www.franklinwatts.co.uk